Contents

Welcome to

As a parent, you want to give your child all the necessary tools for reading success. And research shows that phonics—or the relationship between sounds and their spellings—is an essential one! By teaching kids how to unlock the mysteries of print, we help them discover the joy of reading and send them on their way to becoming confident, lifelong learners.

Toward that end, we created *Phonics Tales*. Each of the 25 stories focuses on a different phonics element—or sound-symbol relationship—including short vowels, long vowels, vowel pairs, consonant blends, digraphs, and more. By devoting an entire story to a single sound, there is a high probability your child will *really* learn it. And, as all great teachers know, internalizing key spelling patterns sets the stage for reading fluency.

This *Phonics Tales* collection is the perfect way for kids to enjoy rollicking tales as they develop reading agility. The stories will help your child . . .

- reinforce common sound-spelling relationships.
- develop decoding and word recognition skills.
- boost phonemic awareness skills (the awareness that words are made up of different sounds).
- build oral language and listening skills.
- expand vocabulary and word knowledge.
- learn letter patterns to become adept spellers.
- cultivate early comprehension skills.

Phonics Tales offers a playful way to capitalize on your child's natural interest in learning to read. This collection contains one story for each of 25 important phonics elements—from short *a* to bossy *r*. The fun stories provide opportunities for your child to develop important phonics and decoding knowledge, while enjoying a language-rich reading experience.

This *Phonics Tales* collection is filled with unique features to fast-track literacy learning including . . .

- kid-pleasing stories packed with bolded words that target a must-know sound such as short *e*, long *u*, the vowel pair *ou*, or the blend *st*.
- interactive activities at the end of each story that invite your child to answer ten riddles using words with the featured phonics element.
- easy-to-learn rhyming cheers to celebrate learning and ensure your child has lots of practice with the target sound.

Mastering early phonics has never been easier or more entertaining! Everything you need to open the gate to literacy success is here. So get ready to savor the stories and read on for some quick tips to maximize learning before, during, and after reading.

Happy learning!

The Editors

Using the Stories

Before Reading

Introduce the featured phonics element of each story with this quick routine.

- Explore the story's "cover" page. Have your child use the title and the illustration to make predictions about what the tale will be about. This will boost early comprehension skills.

- Introduce the featured phonics element shown on the "cover" page of the story. For example, for the story *That Cat Max*, introduce the short-*a* sound. Ask your child to name all the words in the title that have the target sound *(That, cat, Max)*. Can your child think of other words that make the same sound?

- Explain to your child that this story has lots of words with the target sound and those words appear in boldface type. Skim the story and look for them. Invite your child to point to some of the words as you read them together. Say and hold each sound in the word, blending the sounds together. For example, for the word *Max*, you would say, "MMMMMaaaaaxxxxxxxxx." Then have your child repeat the word.

During Reading

- The first time, read the selected tale aloud all the way through. Let your child enjoy the story and get a feel for the language.

- Reread the story, asking your child to look and listen for words with the featured phonics sound—that is, the words in boldface type. If you like, invite him or her to signal when those words are read with a clap. Also, pause to read the Phonics Fact, encouraging your child to answer any questions posed.

- Next, invite your child to closely examine the illustration on each page. Does he or she see anything pictured whose name contains the featured phonics sound? (For example, the picture on the first page of *That Cat Max* includes a *cat* and a *hat*.)

- In addition, encourage your child to chime in on predictable words, especially those containing the featured phonics sound. You may need to pause before the word as you point to it and then help to sound it out. Children always delight in seeing how many words they know and can learn!

After Reading

- Allow your child time to reflect on what he or she liked about the story as well as to share comments. Boost comprehension by asking questions that focus on your child's understanding of the story such as, "Do you think the cat in *That Cat Max* is real or pretend? Why do you think that?"

- Share the page of riddles at the end of the story. Challenge your child to answer the riddles by reading the words in the Word Box and choosing the correct word. (Read the words in the Word Box aloud if necessary.) For added fun, write more words with the target sound on slips of paper, then work with your child to create riddle clues for those words!

- Enjoy the cheer that accompanies each story. Make a mini-megaphone out of rolled up paper and invite your child to shout it out! To extend learning, write the cheer on a separate sheet of paper, leaving blanks for each target word. Then challenge your child to fill in the blanks or to slot in brand-new target words.

- Play a quick game to reinforce the target phonics sound. For example, if the story is about the *fl* blend, say words that begin with that sound—such as *fly*—and words that don't—such as *crab*—challenging your child to clap only for the *fl* words.

Quick Phonics Games

To reinforce phonics learning, try one or all of these playful activities with your child.

Phonics Tales Around the Room

Each time you read a *Phonics Tale*, invite your child to search the room for items with the same target sound. You can also give your child clues, such as, "I spy something that begins with the blend *cl*. It's hanging on the wall. It tells the time." *(clock)*

Tongue-Twister Fun

Make up a tongue twister after sharing a story. For example, for *Shelly's New Shoes*, you might write the following: "Shoeless Shelly shopped for sharp, shiny shoes." Say it once slowly and then invite your child to try to say it quickly. For added fun, ask your child to make up his or her own tongue twister for you to say.

Silly Sentences

Write silly sentences on a sheet of paper, in which the underlined word is one or two letters different from the correct answer. Challenge your child to change the letter(s) to form a word that will make sense in the sentence. Here is an example:

Lucky Duck had pancakes for branch. *(brunch)*

The trolls traveled by grain to the lake. *(train)*

Super Sequel

Choose a favorite character from a *Phonics Tale* and work with your child to write a short sequel. For example, what happens to Jen from *The Best Nest* after she locates the perfect nest? On a sheet of paper, write the story together, being sure to include lots of the target sound (short *e*).

Phonics Tales!™

short a

That Cat Max

by Liza Charlesworth
illustrated by Stephen Lewis

Phonics Fact

The letter *a* is a vowel. A vowel can make a short sound. The short-*a* sound is found in words such as **that, cat**, and **Max**. What other short-*a* words can you find in this story? Look at the pictures, too!

I **am** a **fan** of **that cat Max**. Why?

Max can play **catch**.

Max can cut the **grass**.

Max can chat with **Sandy Blat** about her **brand**-new **tan hat**.

Max can do **crafts**. He made **that fancy basket**.

Phonics Fact

Sometimes the short-*a* sound comes in the second syllable of a word, such as sub**tracts**.

Max can do **math**! He **adds and subtracts** super **fast**!

Max can cook **ham and mashed yams** in a little **black pan**.

Max can drive the **van** to the **snack stand**.
The **apple** pie there is **grand**!

Max has talent! He **can tap and rap**.

Max can also play **sax** in my **dad's jazz band**.

Max can even **act** like **an acrobat**!

But the best thing **Max can** do…

. . . is **nap** on my **lap**. **Man,** I love **that cat Max**!

Short-a Riddles

Listen to the riddles. Then match each riddle with the right short-*a* word from the box.

Word Box

fast	grass	cat	tap	jam
nap	acrobat	hat	can	subtract

1. This pet says, "Meow!"
2. It is the opposite of *slow*.
3. This is a lot like jelly.
4. It is the opposite of *can't*.
5. Sleepy babies do this in a crib.

6. You put this on your head to keep warm.
7. It is green and grows in backyards.
8. A person who does gymnastics is called this.
9. It is the opposite of *add*.
10. A kind of dancing that makes a lot of noise.

Answers: 1. cat 2. fast 3. jam 4. can 5. nap 6. hat 7. grass 8. acrobat 9. subtract 10. tap

Short-a Cheer

Hooray for short *a,* the best sound around!

Let's holler short-*a* words all over town!

There's **map** and **plant** and **rap** and **cat**.

There's **pan** and **band** and **stamp** and **hat**.

There's **man** and **grass** and **jazz** and **tap**.

There's **act** and **fast** and **snap** and **clap**.

Short *a,* short *a,* give a great cheer,

For the **happiest** sound that you ever will hear!

Make a list of other short-*a* words. Then use them in your cheer.

Phonics Tales!™

short e

The Best Nest

by Liza Charlesworth
illustrated by Kelly Kennedy

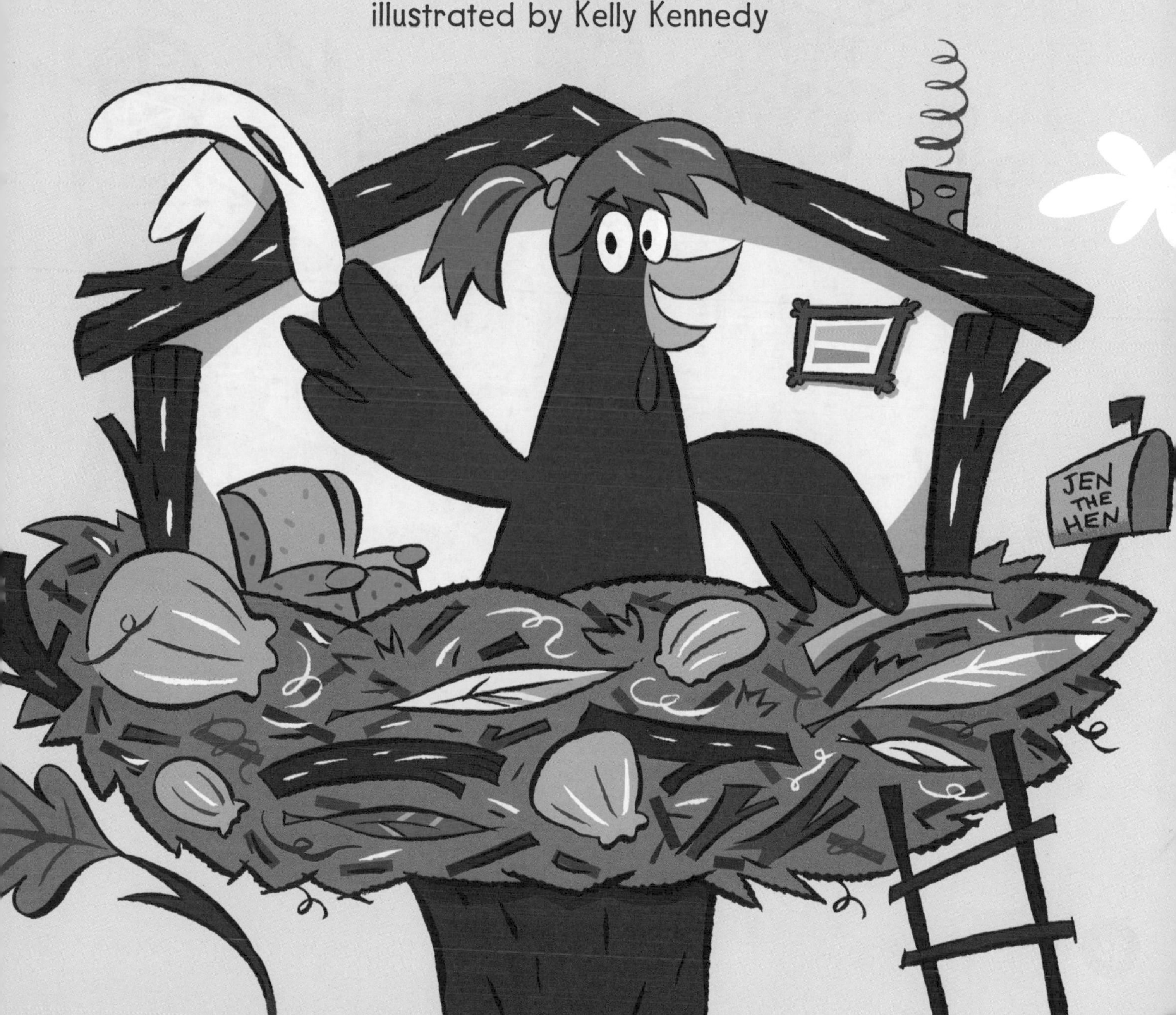

Phonics Fact

The letter *e* is a vowel. A vowel can make a short sound. The short-*e* sound is found in words such as **red**, **hen**, and **Jen**. What other short-*e* words can you find in this story? Look at the pictures, too!

This **red hen** is named **Jen**.

Phonics Fact

Sometimes the short-*e* sound comes in the second syllable of a word, such as in par**ents**.

One day, **Jen** decided to **get** her own **nest**. She packed a **chest** with the **help** of her **parents**, **Ben** and **Bess**.

Jen pecked them good-bye. Then she **set** out **west** to find the **best nest**.

Jen saw a pig **pen** and **went** inside. But that **pen** was a **mess**! It was not the **best nest**.

Jen saw a **tent** and **went** inside. But the **tent** belonged to **ten elves**! It was not the **best nest**.

Jen saw a **shed** and **went** inside. But the **shed** was **bent** and **let** all the rain in! **Jen** got very, very **wet**.

Phonics Fact

A word can have more than one short-*e* sound. The word **excellent** has three!

It was **definitely** not the **best nest**. **Then**, **Jen** got an **excellent** idea.

Phonics Fact

Sometimes the short-*e* sound is made by the letters *ea* as in **thread**. Can you find another *ea* word on this page that makes the short-*e* sound?

(Answer: **feathers**)

Jen found sticks and **stems** and **shells** and **thread** and **feathers** and even some **french** fries.

Jen made **them** into a **nest**.

Next, **Jen** built a **desk** and a **bench** and a cozy **bed** for taking a **rest**.

Then, Jen invited her **very** first **guests**.

Jen served an **elegant** meal of **fresh** worms and **ketchup**.

"I **bet** my **nest** is the **best** in the **West**," said **Jen**.
"**Yes**! **Yes**!" agreed **Ben** and **Bess**.
They were so **impressed**!

Short-e Riddles

Listen to the riddles. Then match each riddle with the right short-*e* word from the box.

Word Box

yes	pen	bench	wet	red
shell	hen	bed	nest	ketchup

1. This is the word for a *girl chicken*.
2. A strawberry is this color.
3. You might search for one at the beach.
4. It means the opposite of *no*.
5. You put this on french fries.
6. A bird builds one in a tree.
7. Pigs live in this place.
8. You sleep on one at night.
9. It means the opposite of *dry*.
10. You can sit on this at the park.

Answers: 1. hen 2. red 3. shell 4. yes 5. ketchup 6. nest 7. pen 8. bed 9. wet 10. bench

Short-e Cheer

Hooray for short *e*, the best sound around!

Let's holler short-*e* words all over town!

There's **west** and **next** and **red** and **hen**.

There's **net** and **fresh** and **nest** and **men**.

There's **best** and **bench** and **shelf** and **send**.

There's **mess** and **spell** and **yes** and **end**.

Short *e*, short *e*, give a great cheer,

For the most **elegant** sound you ever will hear!

Make a list of other short-*e* words. Then use them in your cheer.

Phonics Tales!™

short i

The Little Pink Pig

by Liza Charlesworth
illustrated by Doug Jones

Phonics Fact

The letter *i* is a vowel. A vowel can make a short sound. The short-*i* sound is found in words such as **pink**, **pig**, and **Kim**. What other short-*i* words can you find in this story? Look at the pictures, too!

Once upon a time, there **lived** a **little pink pig**. Her name was **Kim**.

Kim did not like being **little** or **pink**. And she really **did** not like the **dimple in** her **chin**.

One day, **Kim** met a fairy named **Jill**.
"I **will give** you **six wishes**," said Fairy **Jill**.

"**Yippee**!" said **Kim**.
She **slipped** a **wish list** from her purse.

Phonics Fact

Sometimes a word can have more than one short-*i* sound, as in **zippity**.

"My first **wish is** to be **big** like a **hippo**," said **Kim**. **Zippity zip**! Fairy **Jill did it**!

"My second **wish is** to have green **skin** like a **lizard**," said **Kim**.
Zippity zip! Fairy **Jill did it**!

"My third **wish is** to have **thick** feathers like a **chicken**," said **Kim**.
Zippity zip! Fairy **Jill did it**!

"My fourth **wish is** to have a **swishy** tail like a **fish**," said **Kim**.
Zippity zip! Fairy **Jill did it**!

"My **fifth wish is** to have a cute **chin** like a **chimp**," said **Kim**.
Zippity zip! Fairy **Jill did it**!

Kim looked **in** the **silver mirror**.
"**Ick**! I'm so **mixed** up," cried **Kim**.
"I **think** I **miss** the old me!"

Then **Kim** remembered! She **still** had one **wish** left to **fix** her **mistake**.

"My **sixth wish is** to be me again," said **Kim with** a **grin**.
Zippity zip! Fairy **Jill did it**!

Kim was so **thrilled** to be a **little pink pig with** a **dimple in** her **chin** that she **did** a **big jig**! And **Kim** never **wished** to be **different** again.

Short-i Riddles

Listen to the riddles. Then match each riddle with the right short-*i* word from the box.

Word Box

jig	chicken	pig	wish	chimp
big	fish	grin	pink	mirror

1. This animal says, "Oink, oink!"
2. It means the opposite of *little*.
3. This bird lives on a farm and lays eggs.
4. Many pigs are this color.
5. This is another word for *monkey*.
6. You look in one to comb your hair.
7. This animal has fins and a tail.
8. This word means almost the same thing as *smile*.
9. A leprechaun does this kind of dance.
10. A fairy grants this with her magic wand.

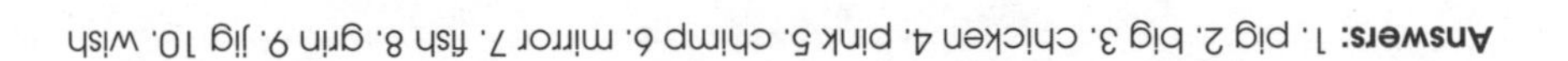

Short-i Cheer

Hooray for short *i*, the best sound around!

Let's holler short-*i* words all over town!

There's **pig** and **trip** and **wish** and **miss**.

There's **lip** and **fish** and **drink** and **dish**.

There's **skip** and **milk** and **six** and **big**.

There's **pink** and **chimp** and **dish** and **wig**.

Short *i*, short *i*, give a great cheer,

For the most **interesting** sound you ever **will** hear!

Make a list of other short-*i* words. Then use them in your cheer.

short o

Todd's Odd Day

by Maria Fleming
illustrated by Kelly Kennedy

Phonics Fact

The letter *o* is a vowel. A vowel can make a short sound. The short-*o* sound is found in words such as **Todd**, **block**, and **lots**. What other short-*o* words can you find in this story? Look at the pictures, too!

One day, **Todd** went for a walk around the **block**. He saw **lots** of **odd** things.

He saw a **hog** and a **dog** out for a **jog**.
"How **odd**!" said **Todd**.

Phonics Fact

A word can have more than one short-*o* sound in it. Which words on this page have two short-*o* sounds?

(Answer: **ocelots, hopscotch**)

He saw **ocelots** with **lots** of **spots**.
"How **odd**!" said **Todd**.

He saw an **ostrich** dressed in **socks** with **dots**.
"How **odd**!" said **Todd**.

He saw a **lobster** leaving a **shop** with a **lollipop**.
"How **odd**!" said **Todd**.

He saw a **crocodile** buy a **doll** for his **tot**.
"How **odd**!" said **Todd**.

He saw a **fox bebop** with a **mop**.
"How **odd**!" said **Todd**.

He saw an **ox** mail a **box** of **rocks**.
"How **odd**!" said **Todd**.

He saw **frogs** playing **soccer** in a parking **lot**.
"How **odd**!" said **Todd**.

He saw a **cop stop** an **otter on** a **log**.
"How **odd**!" said **Todd**.

Suddenly, **Todd** heard a **knock**. He **popped** up in bed. "Wake up!" said his **mom**. **Todd** had been asleep!

Todd got dressed. He **trotted** down the stairs. **Todd's odd** day had just been an **odd** dream!

I am **fond** of **hotcakes**.
I like **hotcakes**, a **lot**, too!
OCTOPUS ESCAPES FROM AQUARIUM
APRICOT JAM

Or maybe **not**!

Short-o Riddles

Listen to the riddles. Then match each riddle with the right short-*o* word from the box.

Word Box

jog	pot	mop	lollipop	socks
hog	top	hot	rock	tot

1. This is the opposite of *cold*.
2. You put these on your feet.
3. This is another word for *a young child*.
4. You do this when you run slowly.
5. This is another word for *pig*.
6. You can cook things in this.
7. This is the opposite of *bottom*.
8. This is another word for *stone*.
9. People use this to clean the floor.
10. This is a sweet treat that you lick.

Answers: 1. hot 2. socks 3. tot 4. jog 5. hog 6. pot 7. top 8. rock 9. mop 10. lollipop

Short-o Cheer

Hooray for short *o*, the best sound around!

Let's holler short-*o* words all over town!

There's **hog** and **tot** and **box** and **rock**.

There's **hop** and **fox** and **doll** and **lock**.

There's **chop** and **cot** and **mom** and **pop**.

There's **clock** and **job** and **pot** and **mop**.

Short *o*, short *o*, give a great cheer,

For the **jolliest** sound you ever will hear!

Make a list of other short-*o* words. Then use them in your cheer.

Phonics Tales!™

short u

Lucky Duck

by Teddy Slater
illustrated by Kellie Lewis

Phonics Fact

The letter *u* is a vowel. A vowel can make a short sound. The short-*u* sound is found in words such as **duck**, **up**, and **luck**. What other short-*u* words can you find in this story? Look at the pictures, too!

One **sunny Sunday**, **Duck** woke **up** in **such** a great mood. He had a **hunch** this would be his **lucky** day.

Phonics Fact

Sometimes the short-*u* sound comes in the second syllable of a word, such as in sy**rup**.

Duck rushed downstairs. He was **hungry** for **plum** pancakes with plenty of **butter** and **syrup**.

Duck opened the **cupboard**. **Uh-oh**! No **plums**.

So **Duck jumped** in his **truck** and headed to **Gus's** Store to get some **plums**. **But** the **truck** hit a **bump** and would not **budge**.

When **Duck** got out of his **truck—yuck**!
He stepped in a big **puddle** of **mud**.

"I will **just** have to walk," said **Duck**. **But** along the way, he got **stuck** in **bubble gum**. **Ugh**!

Still, **Duck trudged** on. That is, **until** he got **stung** on the **thumb** by a **bumblebee**. What an **ugly lump**!

By the time **Duck** got to **Gus's** Store, his **tummy** was **rumbling**. He was very **hungry**, **plus** very **grumpy**.

Duck had never felt less **lucky**. Then, **uh-oh**!
He dropped his **plums**.

But suddenly. . . **Duck** heard a **drum** roll. Then **Gus** said, "Congratulations! You are the one **hundredth customer** of the **summer**."

Gus gave **Duck** a **hug** and a coupon for a free **brunch** at the **Snug** Diner on **Huff** Street.

Duck rushed off to the **Snug** Diner and placed his order: a stack of **plum** pancakes with plenty of **butter** and **syrup**.

Yum! It was **just** what he wanted.
Oh, what a **lucky duck**!

Short-u Riddles

Listen to the riddles. Then match each riddle with the right short-*u* word from the box.

Word Box

yum	duck	snug	luck	up
jump	plum	Sunday	butter	summer

1. This animal says, "Quack, quack."
2. You put this on toast or popcorn.
3. This is the day after Saturday.
4. It is the opposite of *down*.
5. This word rhymes with *rug*.
6. A four-leaf clover brings this.
7. It means almost the same thing as *leap*.
8. This is the season after spring.
9. You say this when something is delicious.
10. This purple fruit is bigger than a grape.

Answers: 1. duck 2. butter 3. Sunday 4. up 5. snug 6. luck 7. jump, 8. summer 9. yum 10. plum

Short-u Cheer

Hooray for short *u*, the best sound around!

Let's holler short-*u* words all over town!

There's **mug** and **sun** and **lunch** and **up**.

There's **gum** and **fun** and **luck** and **cup**.

There's **bug** and **hut** and **hum** and **rug**.

There's **lump** and **run** and **chum** and **hug**.

Short *u*, short *u*, give a great cheer,

For the **luckiest** sound you ever will hear!

Make a list of other short-*u* words. Then use them in your cheer.

Phonics Tales!™

long a

Jake and Jane's Great Race

by Pamela Chanko
illustrated by Kellie Lewis

Phonics Fact

This story is full of long-*a* words. Many times this sound is made by a silent *e*. The vowel *a* is followed by a consonant, which is then followed by a silent *e*, as in **Jake** and **Jane**. What other long-*a* words can you find in this story? Look at the pictures, too!

Jake Snake was in super **shape**. So **Jake** challenged his friends **Jane** and **Abe** to **race** around **Drake Lake**.

Phonics Fact

The long-*a* sound can also be made by the letters *ay*, as in **way** and **okay**. Can you find another word on this page that uses *ay* to stand for long *a*?

(Answer: **today**)

"No **way**!" said **Abe**.
But **Jane** said, "**Okay**! Let's **race today**!"
That **Jane** sure was **brave**!

Phonics Fact

The vowel pair *ai* can make the long-*a* sound, too. Words that use *ai* to stand for long *a* include **wait, paid,** and **claim**.

Everyone **came** to see the **race**.
"I'm so **amazing**! I can't **wait** to win!" boasted **Jake**.
"You **may** be surprised!" replied **Jane**.

The two **racers** took their **places**.
"Ready, set, go!" yelled **Abe**.

Jane raced and **raced**.

Phonics Fact

The long-*a* sound is sometimes made with an *ea*, as in **break** and **great**. And guess what? A stand-alone *a* can make the long-*a* sound, too!

But **Jake** took **a break** to **bake a layer cake**.

Jane raced and **raced**.

But **Jake** took **a break** to **make a quaint painting** of **Drake Lake**.

Jane raced and **raced**.

But **Jake** took **a break** to call his friend **named Dave**, who lived in **Spain**.

Jane raced and **raced**.

But **Jake** took **a break** and **ate a** big **plate** of **grapes**!
Then he heard **Abe say**, "**Hey**, **Jane** is winning!"
That **made Jake** decide to join the **race**.

But it was **way** too **late**. **Jane** won first **place**!
"You did **great**! Want to **make a statement**?" asked **Abe**.
"Slow and steady wins the **race**," said **Jane**.

Long-a Riddles

Listen to the riddles. Then match each riddle with the right long-*a* word from the box.

Word Box

snake	paint	day	late	brave
cake	Jake	grapes	plate	race

1. It is the opposite of *early*.
2. It is the opposite of *fearful*.

3. You dip a brush in this to make a picture.
4. Your birthday candles go on top of this.
5. This animal slithers and makes a hissing sound.
6. This fruit comes in a bunch.
7. This boy's name rhymes with *bake*.
8. You can run in this kind of contest.
9. This is round and you put food on it.
10. It is the opposite of *night*.

Answers: 1. late 2. brave 3. paint 4. cake 5. snake 6. grapes 7. Jake 8. race 9. plate 10. day

Long-a Cheer

Hooray for long *a*, the best sound around!

Let's holler long-*a* words all over town!

There's **ape** and **date** and **jay** and **snake**.

There's **brave** and **grape** and **bake** and **cake**.

There's **day** and **say** and **stain** and **quaint**.

There's **great** and **break** and **chain** and **paint**.

Long *a*, long *a*, give **a great** cheer

For the most **amazing** sound you'll ever hear!

Make a list of other long-*a* words. Then use them in your cheer.

long e

Queen Bee's Scream

by Liza Charlesworth
illustrated by Patrick Girouard

Phonics Fact

This story is full of long-*e* words. One common spelling of the long-*e* sound is *ee*, as in **meet**, **queen**, and **bee**. What other long-*e* words can you find in this story? Look at the pictures, too!

Meet Queen Bee.

Phonics Fact

The vowel pair *ea* can also make the long-*e* sound, as in **mean**. Can you find another word on this page that uses *ea* to stand for the long-*e* sound?

(Answer: **screamed**)

Everyone thought **Queen Bee** was **mean because she screamed**.

Phonics Fact

The long-*e* sound can be made with a single *e*, too. Words that follow this spelling pattern include **she**, **he**, **me**, and **be**.

"**Feed** our pet **flea**!" **she screamed** at **Jean Bee**.
But **Jean Bee** buzzed away.

"**Sweep** up **these leaves**!" **she screamed**
at **Lee Bee**.
But **Lee Bee** buzzed away.

"**Weed** the **bean** garden!" **she screamed** at **Sheena Bee**.
But **Sheena Bee** buzzed away.

"**Clean** our hive until it **gleams**!" **she screamed** at **Dee Bee**.
But **Dee Bee** buzzed away.

Phonics Fact

When a word ends in *y*, the *y* sometimes makes a long-*e* sound, as in **Benny**. Can you find another word on this page that uses a *y* to stand for the long-*e* sound?

(Answer: **majesty**)

"Make some **peach tea**!" **she screamed** at **Benny Bee**.

But **Benny Bee** DID NOT **flee**. **He** just made her **majesty** some **tea**.

Phonics Fact

The long-*e* sound is sometimes made by the vowel pair *ie*, as in **believe**. Other long-*e* words with this spelling pattern include **chief** and **niece**.

"**Benny**, I **need** to ask you something!" **screamed Queen Bee**. "Why do all the **bees speed** away when I **speak**?"

"I **believe** the **reason** is that you **scream**," **squeaked Benny Bee.**

"I **see**," said **Queen Bee**. "I was just using my outdoor voice so all the **bees** could hear **me**. From now on, I will **speak softly**."

"**Neat**!" **squeaked Benny Bee**. "And there's one more thing: "When you **need** our help, would you say **please**?"

"That is **easy**," said **Queen Bee**. "**Please** go tell the **bees** to **meet me beneath** the **tree** for a **speech**."

"I will **be** back **before** you can count to **three**," **squeaked Benny Bee**.

"**My sweet bees,** I am **really** sorry that I **screamed** and did not say **please,**" said **Queen Bee softly**. "Can you **each** forgive **me**?"

"YES, **INDEED**!" **screamed** the **bees**.
"**We** love you, **Queen Bee**!"

Long-e Riddles

Listen to the riddles. Then match each riddle with the right long-*e* word from the box.

Word Box				
queen	sweet	flea	bee	mean
clean	scream	leaves	sweep	bean

1. This bug has black and yellow stripes.
2. A princess grows up to be this.
3. It is the opposite of *dirty*.
4. You do this with a broom.
5. It is the opposite of *sour*.
6. It is the opposite of *nice*.
7. These grow on the branches of trees.
8. It means almost the same thing as *yell*.
9. This vegetable rhymes with *mean*.
10. This bug sometimes makes dogs itch.

Answers: 1. bee 2. queen 3. clean 4. sweep 5. sweet 6. mean 7. leaves 8. scream 9. bean 10. flea

Long-e Cheer

Hooray for long *e*, the best sound around!

Let's holler long-*e* words all over town!

There's **queen** and **bee** and **cheese** and **scream**.

There's **clean** and **read** and **tea** and **dream**.

There's **me** and **we** and **she** and **he**.

There's **brief** and **chief** and **deep** and **sea**.

Long *e*, long *e*, give a great cheer

For the **neatest** sound you ever will hear!

Make a list of other long-*e* words. Then use them in your cheer.

Phonics Tales!™

long i

Ike and Mike

by Maria Fleming
illustrated by Kelly Kennedy

Phonics Fact

This story is full of long-*i* words. Many times this sound is made by a silent *e*. The vowel *i* is followed by a consonant, which is then followed by a silent *e*, as in **Ike** and **Mike**. What other long-*i* words can you find in this story? Look at the pictures, too!

This is **Ike**. This is **Ike's** brother, **Mike**.

Ike does not **like** to share with **Mike**.
Mike does not **like** to share with **Ike**.

Phonics Fact

The long-*i* sound can also be made with a single *i* as in I. Another word with this spelling pattern is **hi**.

Ike has a new **white bike**.
"Can **I ride** your **bike**?" **Mike** asks **Ike**.
"No way!" says **Ike**. "It's **mine**!"

Phonics Fact

Sometimes the letter *y* makes the long-*i* sound, as in **fly** and **sky**. Can you find two other words on this page with *y* that make the long-*i* sound?

(Answer: **try, my**)

Mike likes to **fly** his **kite** in the **sky**.
"Can **I try** to **fly** your **kite**?" **Ike** asks **Mike**.
"No way!" says **Mike**. "It's **mine**!"

Phonics Fact

The vowel pair *ie* can also make the long-*i* sound, as in **fries**. Can you find another long-*i* word with the same spelling pattern on this page?

(Answer: **pie**)

At **lunchtime**, **Ike** has French **fries**. **Mike** has **lime pie**.

"Can **I try** a **fry**?" **Mike** asks **Ike**.

"No way!" says **Ike**. "It's **mine**! Can **I try** a **bite** of **pie**?"
"No way!" says **Mike**. "It's **mine**!"

Ike and **Mike spy** a toy. They each have **five dimes**. Will they share their **dimes** to get the toy? No way!

Phonics Fact

Another spelling pattern that makes the long-*i* sound is *igh*, as in **fight**. Other words with this pattern are **sigh**, **might**, and **right**. Be on the lookout for more!

Ike and **Mike** begin to **fight**.

Then **Ike** and **Mike** begin to **cry**. A **wise fly** buzzes **by**.
"Boys, take **my advice**," he says with a **sigh**.
"It's **nice** to share."

"That **fly might** just be **right**," says **Ike**.
"Let's give it a **try**," says **Mike**.

Ike and **Mike** think sharing is **mighty fine**!

That **night**, **Ike** shares his book of **rhymes** with **Mike**. **Mike** shares his stuffed **lion**, **Spike**, with **Ike**.

The **fly smiles** with **delight** as he turns out the **light**. "What a **sight**! Sleep **tight**! Good **night**!"

Long-i Riddles

Listen to the riddles. Then match each riddle with the right long-*i* word from the box.

Word Box

fly	dime	bite	smile	pie
hi	wise	lime	bike	night

1. You do this when you are happy.
2. This is something you eat for dessert.
3. You can buy things with this coin.
4. This is a bug.
5. This has wheels and you can ride it.
6. It means *smart*.
7. It is the opposite of *day*.

8. This green fruit tastes sour.
9. It means the same thing as *hello*.
10. You do this when you eat an apple.

Answers: 1. smile 2. pie 3. dime 4. fly 5. bike 6. wise 7. night 8. lime 9. hi 10. bite

Long-i Cheer

Hooray for long *i*, the best sound around!

Let's holler long-*i* words all over town!

There's **like** and **nice** and **bike** and **kite**.

There's **fly** and **sky** and **light** and **night**.

There's **pie** and **my** and **five** and **find**.

There's **write** and **rice** and **size** and **kind**.

Long *i*, long *i*, give a great cheer

For the **finest** sound you ever will hear!

Make a list of other long-*i* words. Then use them in your cheer.

Phonics Tales!™

long o

At Home With Mole and Toad

by Maria Fleming
illustrated by Doug Jones

Phonics Fact

This story is full of long-*o* words. Many times this sound is made by a silent *e*. The vowel *o* is followed by a consonant, which is then followed by a silent *e*, as in **mole** and **hole**. What other long-*o* words can you find in this story? Look at the pictures, too!

Mole lives in a **hole**. Her friend **Toad** lives down the **road**.

Phonics Fact

The vowel pair *oa* can also make the long-*o* sound, as in **toad** and **road**. Can you find two words in the picture that use *oa* to stand for the long-*o* sound?

(Answer: **goat, boat**)

One day, **Toad phones Mole**.

Phonics Fact

A single *o* can also make the long-*o* sound, as in **over** and **okay**. Try to spot other words that use one *o* to make the long-*o* sound.

"**Won't** you come **over** for **toast** and **cocoa**," asks **Toad**.
"**Okay**!" says **Mole**.

Phonics Fact

The spelling pattern *ow* is another way to make the long-*o* sound, as in **show** and **yellow**. **Grow** and **snow** are other long-*o* words that follow this pattern. Be on the lookout for more!

Mole wants to **show** **Toad** her new **yellow** skates. So she puts them on and **rolls** down the **road**.

Mole rolls down a **slope**. She **rolls over** a **hose**. Then **Mole rolls over** the **roses Toad grows**.

Mole rolls into **Toad's home**. She **rolls** into a table and knocks **over** the **cocoa** and **toast**.

Phonics Fact

The vowel pair *oe*—as in **Joe**—can make the long-*o* sound, too. Can you find a long-*o* word with this spelling pattern on the next page?

(Answer: **toe**)

Mole rolls into a shelf. She knocks **over Toad's snow globes**. She spills the **bowl** that **holds Mole's goldfish**, **Joe**.

Mole even **rolls** right **over Toad's toe**! **Toad moans** and **groans**. He **scolds Mole**, "**No** more **rolling**! **Mole**, you must **go**!"

Mole rolls home, feeling **low**.

The next day, **Mole phones Toad**.
"I am **so**, **so**, **so**, **so**, **so**, **so** sorry," says **Mole**.

"That is **okay**," says **Toad**. "I **know** you did not mean to **roll over** everything. I **know** you did not mean to hurt **Joe** or my **toe**."

Toad invites **Mole over** for **oatmeal** cookies and **cold** milk. How will **Mole go** down the **road** to **Toad's**? Will **Mole roll**?

No! This time, **Mole** will **stroll**!

Long-o Riddles

Listen to the riddles. Then match each riddle with the right long-*o* word from the box.

Word Box

toad	toes	phone	cold	go
road	mole	toast	rose	snow

1. This is white and falls from the sky.
2. This small, furry animal lives in a hole.
3. It is the opposite of *stop*.
4. It means the same as *street*.
5. This tastes good with butter on it.
6. You have five of these on each foot.
7. It is a kind of flower.
8. You use it to talk to someone.
9. This animal is a lot like a frog.
10. It is the opposite of *hot*.

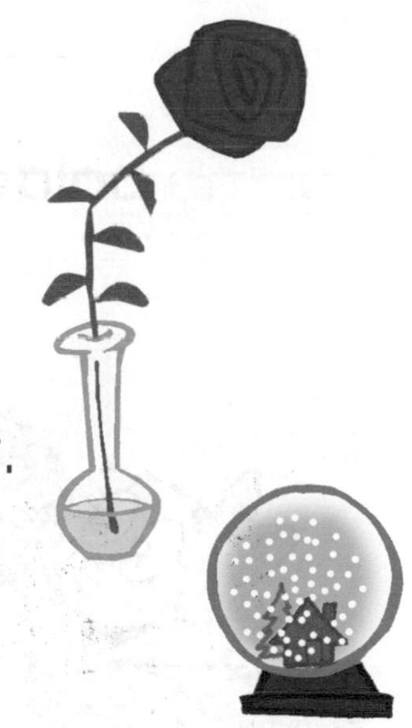

Answers: 1. snow 2. mole 3. go 4. road 5. toast 6. toes 7. rose 8. phone 9. toad 10. cold

Long-o Cheer

Hooray for long *o*, the best sound around!

Let's holler long-*o* words all over town!

There's **mole** and **hole** and **phone** and **rose**.

There's **toad** and **road** and **home** and **hose**.

There's **snow** and **grow** and **no** and **go**.

There's **cold** and **gold** and **hoe** and **toe**.

Long *o*, long *o*, give a great cheer,

For the **boldest** sound you ever will hear!

Make a list of other long-*o* words. Then use them in your cheer.

Phonics Tales!

long u

A Mule Named Sugar Cube

by Maria Fleming

illustrated by Margaux Lucas

Phonics Fact

This story is full of long-*u* words. Many times this sound is made by a silent *e*. The vowel *u* is followed by a consonant, which is then followed by a silent *e*, as in **cube** and **mule**. What other long-*u* words can you find in this story? Look at the pictures, too!

This is Sugar **Cube**. Sugar **Cube** is a very **cute mule**.

Phonics Fact

The letter *u* does not always need the help of silent *e* to make the long-*u* sound. Sometimes a single *u* makes the sound all by itself. The word **unusual** has two long-*u* sounds in it! Can you find two words in the picture that use a single *u* to make the long-*u* sound?

(Answer: **Hugo's, menu**)

Sugar **Cube** is not like other **mules**.
Sugar **Cube** is **unusual**.

Sugar **Cube** can **use** a **computer**.

Sugar **Cube** loves **music**. She can play the **bugle**.

Sugar **Cube** likes to go to the **museum**.

Sugar **Cube** can ride a **unicycle**.

Phonics Fact

The letters *ew* sometimes make the long-*u* sound, as in **few**. The letters *you* also make the long-*u* sound, as in **youthful**. Can you find other long-*u* words on this page that use these spelling patterns?

(Answer: **mew, Matthew, you**)

One day, a **few youthful mules** call
Sugar **Cube** over.
"**Excuse** me," says a **mule** named **Matthew**.
"But **you** should act like a **regular mule**."

Matthew hurt Sugar **Cube's** feelings. Sugar **Cube** wants to fit in. She wants to be part of the **mule community**.

Sugar **Cube** tries to do **regular mule** things. But it's no **use**. **Regular mule** things do not **amuse** her.

Then Sugar **Cube** gets a **useful** idea.

Sugar **Cube** teaches the other **mules** how to **use** a **computer**. She teaches them how to ride a **unicycle** and play the **bugle**.

Sugar **Cube** even takes the other **mules** to the **museum**. Now Sugar **Cube** is not such an **unusual mule**.

But she is still very **cute**!

Long-u Riddles

Listen to the riddles. Then match each riddle with the right long-*u* word from the box.

Word Box

cube	music	few	museum	menu
mule	huge	you	cute	computer

1. This farm animal looks kind of like a horse.
2. It is the opposite of *me*.
3. You use this to order food at a restaurant.
4. It means *very big*.
5. You can use this to write, play games, or send e-mail.

6. You can see art in this building.
7. This has a square shape.

8. It rhymes with *flute*.
9. It is the opposite of *many*.
10. You hear this on the radio.

Answers: 1. mule 2. you 3. menu 4. huge 5. computer 6. museum 7. cube 8. cute 9. few 10. music

Long-u Cheer

Hooray for long *u*, the best sound around!

Let's holler long-*u* words all over town!

There's **cube** and **cute** and **huge** and **mule**.

There's **music** and **bugle** and **menu** and **fuel**.

There's **fuse** and **fume** and **youth** and **few**.

There's **uniform**, **cucumber**, **perfume**, and **you**.

Long *u*, long *u*, give a great cheer,

For the most **useful** sound **you** ever will hear!

Make a list of other long-*u* words. Then use them in your cheer.

Phonics Tales!

oo

Goo, Goo!

by Teddy Slater
illustrated by Cary Pillo

Phonics Fact

The story you are about to read is full of *oo* words. This pair of vowels is called a digraph. That means the two vowels work together to make a single sound, as in the words **too**, **ooh**, and **goo**, **goo**. What other *oo* words can you find in this story? Look at the pictures, too!

Everyone thinks my brother is **too** cute for words. "Kitchy, kitchy, **coo**!" they say. "**Ooh**, he is so sweet!" they **croon**.

But all my brother says is, "**Goo**, **goo**!" He is **too** little to talk. He just opens up his **googly** eyes. Then he smiles his **goofy** grin and **drools**.

Phonics Fact

Sometimes the *oo* sound appears in the second syllable of a word, as in **raccoon** and **baboon**. Can you find a word on this page with the *oo* sound in the third syllable?

(Answer: **kangaroo**)

My brother's **room** is like a **zoo**. He has a **moose**, a **goose**, a **raccoon**, a **poodle**, a **baboon**, and a big **kangaroo**.

He has an owl that says, "**Hoot**!" and a cow that says, "**Moo**!" Everyone gives him stuffed animals.

But does my brother say thanks? Nope.
He just says, "**Goo, goo**!" That is all he can say:
"**Goo, goo**! **Goo, goo**!"

My brother likes my toys, **too**. I have a car that goes **VROOM** and a plane that goes **ZOOM**. I have a drum that goes **BOOM**! **BOOM**! **BOOM**! And I have a **choo-choo** train with a red **caboose**.

My brother has just one **tooth** so he only eats **gooey foods.** "**Goo, goo**!" he says when you give him a **noodle.** He can't even use a **spoon**!

After lunch, his eyes get **droopy**. Sometimes he even **snoozes** all **afternoon**.

Phonics Fact

Sometimes *oo* is pronounced differently than in the words **too, ooh**, and **goo, goo**. It can also make the sound found in *good, wood,* and *took*. Can you find a word on the next page with the same *oo* sound as in *good*?

(Answer: **books**)

But as **soon** as I come home from **school**, he wakes up. Then he gives me that good old grin and we play and play!

At night, in the **moonlight**, I help Mom put on his **booties**. She reads him fun books like *Winnie the **Pooh***. After that, I **toot** my **kazoo** and sing, "Yankee **Doodle** Dandy."

If he is not in the **mood** to sleep, my brother cries, "**Boo, hoo**! **Boo, hoo**!" My parents try **oodles** of things to make him stop. But I'm the only one who can.

I **scoot** over to his crib, **scoop** him up, and give him a big **smooch**. And just like that, he goes from "**Boo, hoo**!" to "**Goo, goo**!"

That's the **cool** thing about the kid. I love him and he loves me, **too**! If I could pick any brother, I would always **choose** him!

OO Riddles

Listen to the riddles. Then match each riddle with the right *oo* word from the box.

Word Box				
soon	toot	moose	moon	school
moo	boom	poodle	kangaroo	afternoon

1. What a cow says.
2. This animal hops and has a pouch.
3. This is the sound that a train makes.
4. You go to this place to learn.
5. Fireworks make this sound.
6. It means *in a little while*.
7. This animal has big antlers.
8. You can see this in the night sky along with stars.
9. This kind of dog has curly hair.
10. It is the time between morning and night.

Answers: 1. moo 2. kangaroo 3. toot 4. school 5. boom 6. soon 7. moose 8. moon 9. poodle 10. afternoon

OO Cheer

Hooray for o-o, the best pair around!

Let's holler o-o words all over town!

There's **school** and **choose** and **roof** and **moon**.

There's **gloom** and **room** and **scoop** and **soon**.

There's **bloom** and **toot** and **tool** and **noodle**.

There's **boot** and **scoot** and **zoo** and **poodle**.

O-o, o-o, give a great cheer,

For the **grooviest** sound you ever will hear!

Make a list of other *oo* words that make the same sound as these. Then use them in your cheer.

Phonics Tales!™

ou

Mouse in My House!

by Violet Findley
illustrated by Richard Torrey

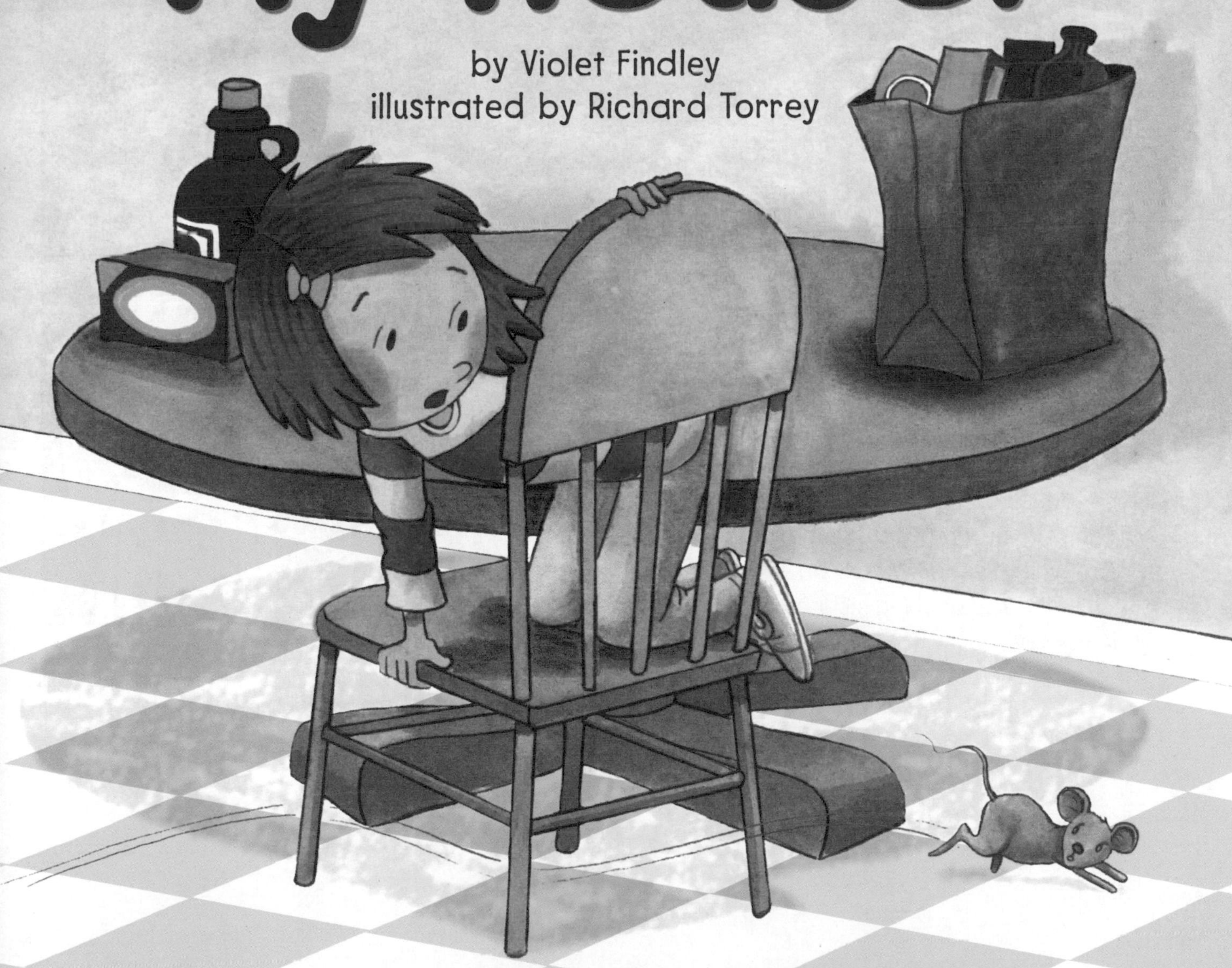

Phonics Fact

The story you are about to read is full of *ou* words. This pair of vowels is called a diphthong. That means the *o* and the *u* work together to make a smooth sound that glides from one vowel sound to the next, as in the words **found**, **mouse**, and **loud**. What other *ou* words can you find in this story? Look at the pictures, too!

This is a story **about** the day I **found** a **mouse** in my **house**. It all started with a **loud** squeaking **sound**.

Phonics Fact

Sometimes the *ou* sound appears in the second syllable of a word, as in **around**. Be on the lookout for more *ou* words like this!

When I looked **around**, I saw a **mouse** on the **counter**.
"EEEEEEEEK!" I **shouted**. "Out of my **house, Mouse**!"

But that **mouse bounded** onto the **ground** and **bounced** off my shoe. "**OUCH**!" I **shouted**.

Next, the **mouse** knocked over a five-**pound** bag of **flour**. Then, he scurried **about**, leaving **clouds** of **flour** all **around**!

"Out of my **house, Mouse**!" I **shouted**.
But that **mouse bounded** onto a **mountain** of clothes and curled up on my best **blouse**!

"**Out** of my **house, Mouse**!" I **shouted**.
But the **mouse bounded** onto a **round** table.
He **pounced** on my **Sour** Gummy Worms and
ate **about** a **thousand**! (I **counted**.)

Then, that **lousy mouse bounded out** of the room. I was **outraged**! Where did he go? I **scouted around** for **hours**.

Well, I never **found** that **mouse** so I plopped on the **couch** to **pout**.

And guess who was **lounging** beside me?
The **mouse**!

When I looked at the **mouse**, he was trembling. Why, that **mouse** was not **lousy** at all! He was just scared.

"I'm sorry I was a **grouch**," I said **loudly**.
Then that **mouse bounded** onto my hand.
"Squeak, squeak!" went his tiny **mouth**.

I am **proud** to say that the **mouse** and I are now pals. In fact, he lives with me in my **house**.

And that **mouse** never bothers me an **ounce**. Except when he **devours** my **Sour** Gummy Worms!

OU Riddles

Listen to the riddles. Then match each riddle with the right *ou* word from the box.

Word Box

loud	sour	mouse	mouth	out
house	shout	found	hour	mountain

1. This tiny, furry animal loves cheese.
2. It is the opposlte of *quiet*.

3. Lemons taste this way.
4. Another word for a *home*.

5. It is the same amount of time as 60 minutes.
6. It is the opposite of *lost*.
7. This means almost the same thing as *yell*.
8. You use this part of your body to eat and talk.
9. It is the opposite of *in*.
10. This is the word for a *very, very tall hill*.

Answers: 1. mouse 2. loud 3. sour 4. house 5. hour 6. found 7. shout 8. mouth 9. out 10. mountain

OU Cheer

Hooray for *o-u*, the best pair around!

Let's holler *o-u* words all over town!

There's **house** and **mouse** and **scout** and **found**.

There's **out** and **pout** and **round** and **ground**.

There's **count** and **south** and **mouth** and **cloud.**

There's **bounce** and **ounce** and **trout** and **proud**.

O-u, o-u, give a great cheer,

For the **loudest sound** you ever will hear!

Make a list of other *ou* words. Then use them in your cheer.

silent e

Porcupine Pete

by Maria Fleming
illustrated by Steve Björkman

Phonics Fact

The words **these**, **Rose**, **Luke**, **Jane**, and **Steve** are all silent-*e* words because you don't hear the *e* at the end of the word. But the silent *e* still has a job to do. It makes the vowel sound in these words a long-vowel sound. What other silent-*e* words can you find in this story? Look at the pictures, too!

My name is **Rose**. **These** are my friends, **Luke**, **Jane**, and **Steve**.

These are my other friends, **Dave**, **Mike**, and **Eve**.

Phonics Fact

Look at the words **pet** and **Pete**. By putting a silent *e* at the end of *pet*, the vowel sound changes from short *e* to long *e*. It makes a new word. Be on the lookout for more silent-*e* words with the long-*e* sound.

They are good friends. But my very best friend is my pet, **Pete**. **Pete** and I do everything together.

Pete is a great **athlete**. We love to **compete**.

Phonics Fact

Look at the words **spin** and **spine**. By putting a silent *e* at the end of *spin*, the vowel sound changes from short *i* to long *i*. It makes a new word. Be on the lookout for more silent-*e* words with the long-*i* sound.

I spin **Pete** on the merry-go-round.
It tickles his **spines**.

We **like** to sit **side**-by-**side** on a double-**wide** **slide**. Down we **glide**!

Phonics Fact

Look at the words **hop** and **hope**. By putting a silent *e* at the end of *hop*, the vowel sound changes from short *o* to long *o*. It makes a new word. Be on the lookout for more silent-*e* words with the long-*o* sound.

Pete and I play hopscotch together.
I **hope** to hop as well as **Pete** one day.

We love to **pose** in silly **clothes**. In a **robe**, I'm a queen on a **throne**. **Pete's** a clown in a **cone** hat and funny **nose**.

Phonics Fact

Look at the words **cap** and **cape**. By putting a silent *e* at the end of *cap*, the vowel sound changes from short *a* to long *a*. It makes a new word. Be on the lookout for more silent-*e* words with the long-*a* sound.

Sometimes we dress in a cap and **cape**.
We pretend we are **brave** superheroes.

Pete and I **make fake cakes** for picnics by the **lake**.

Phonics Fact

Look at the words **hug** and **huge**. By putting a silent *e* at the end of *hug,* the vowel sound changes from short *u* to long *u*. It makes a new word. Be on the lookout for more silent-*e* words with the long-*u* sound.

It can be tricky to give **Pete** a hug.
But it's not a **huge** problem.

We just **use** marshmallows!

Pete is always by my **side**. **Life** would not be **complete** without my pet, **Pete**!

Silent-e Riddles

Listen to the riddles. Then match each riddle with the silent-*e* word from the box.

Word Box

slide	Pete	nose	cake	huge
wide	cape	cute	rose	lake

1. This is a kind of flower.
2. People use this word to describe babies.
3. Superman wears one of these.
4. This is a great place to go fishing.

5. It is a boy's name.
6. You use this to smell.
7. It is the opposite of *narrow*.
8. You eat this sweet treat on your birthday.
9. This means *very big*.
10. You find this at a playground.

Answers: 1. rose 2. cute 3. cape 4. lake 5. Pete 6. nose 7. wide 8. cake 9. huge 10. slide

Silent-e Cheer

Hooray for silent *e* and its long-vowel sound!

Let's holler silent-*e* words all over town!

There's **Pete** and **like**, **concrete** and **slide**.

There's **robe** and **cone** and **bike** and **hide**.

There's **cute** and **cube** and **mule** and **name**.

There's **joke** and **rope** and **cake** and **game**.

Silent *e*! Silent *e*! Let's cheer for a **while**,

For words that always **make** us **smile**!

Make a list of other silent-*e* words. Then use them in your cheer.

Phonics Tales!™

bossy r

Bert's Super Circus

by Liza Charlesworth
illustrated by Stephen Gilpin

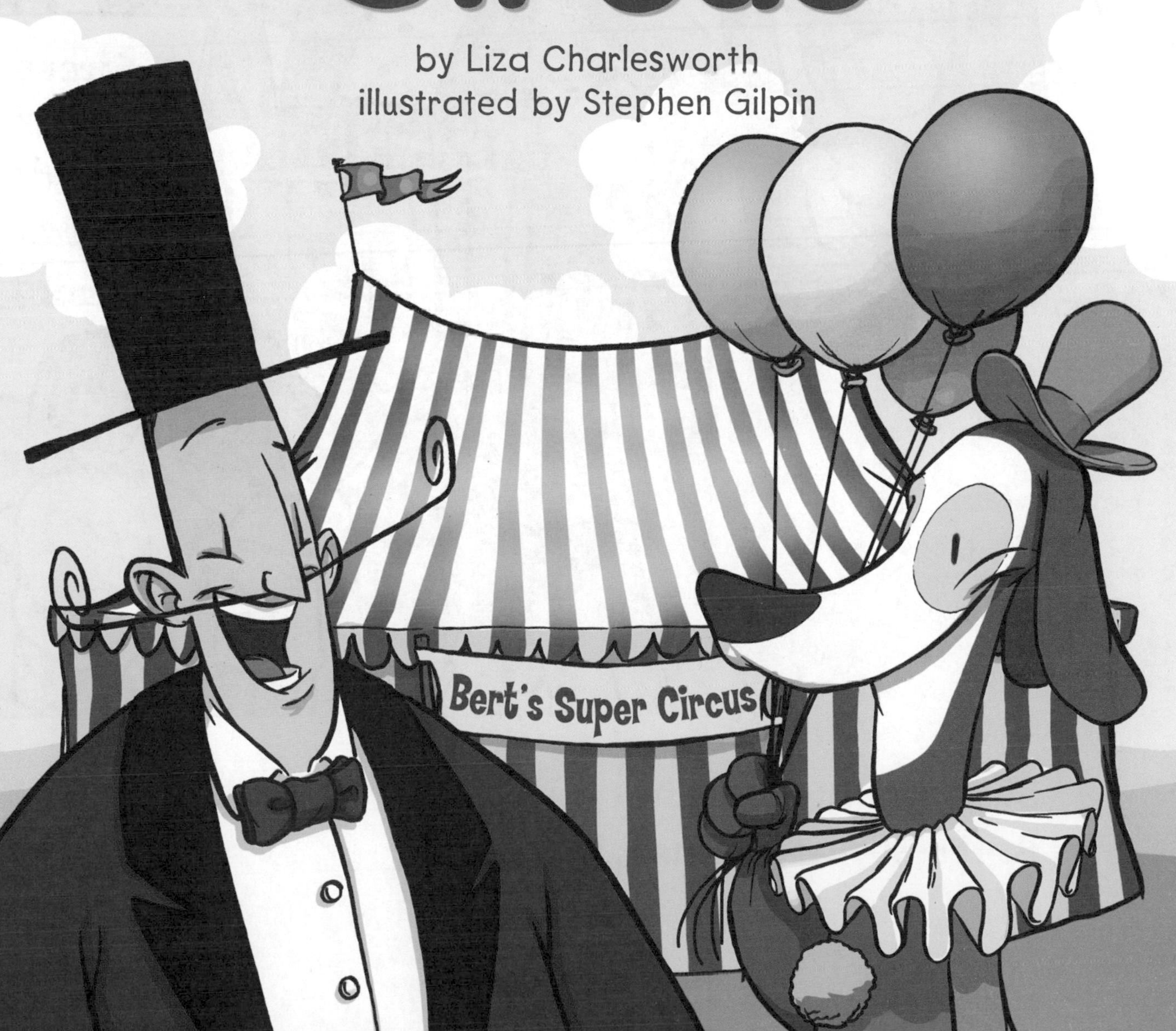

Phonics Fact

Bert, **circus**, **start**, and **turn** are all bossy-*r* words. In bossy-*r* words, the *r* takes charge and changes the sound of the vowel it immediately follows. Say *bet* and *Bert*. *Bet* makes a short-*e* sound. But when *r* is added, as in *Bert*, the *e* makes a very different sound. Can you find more bossy-*r* words in this story? Look at the pictures, too!

Step right up, **gather** round!
Bert's Super Circus is in town!

Boys and **girls** of any age,
to **start** the show, just **turn** the page!

First, a **bird** named **Shirley** will **chirp** "Happy **Birthday**"

as she **whirls** and **twirls** a baton in a **circle**.

Then, a **turtle** named **Kurt** will reach into a magic **urn**

Phonics Fact

Turtle and **Kurt** are both *-ur* words. What others do you see on this page?

and pull out a **furry purple** rabbit with a **curly** tail!

Then, a **serpent** named **Fern** will **enter** a **silver** door

Phonics Fact

Serpent and **Fern** are both *-er* words. What others do you see on this page?

and **emerge perched** on **her** favorite **dessert**!

Then, a **stork** named **Mort** will play an **enormous horn**

Phonics Fact

Stork and **Norm** are both *-or* words. What others do you see on this page?

and use **forty forks** to **form** an amazing **fort**.

Last, a **charming shark** named **Marla** will play **guitar** in a **car**

Phonics Fact

Charming and **shark** are both -*ar* words. What others do you see on this page?

then strum a **harp** atop a **large** cookie **jar**!
What a **star**!

Wow! **Bert's Super Circus** has come to an end. The **performers** do hope you will all come again!

Bossy-r Rid

Listen to the riddles. Then match each riddle with the right bossy-*r* word from the box.

Word Box

stars	fern	large	fork	circle
bird	turtle	circus	serpent	purple

1. This animal flies and chirps.
2. This goes along with a spoon and knife.
3. It is a kind of plant.
4. These shine in the night sky.
5. It is the name for a round shape.
6. This animal is a lot like a tortoise.
7. It is a kind of snake.
8. Some grapes are this color.
9. Clowns, animals, and jugglers are part of this show.
10. It is the opposite of *small*.

Answers: 1. bird 2. fork 3. fern 4. stars 5. circle 6. turtle 7. serpent 8. purple 9. circus 10. large

ossy-r Cheer

Hooray for bossy *r,* the best sound around!

Let's shout bossy-*r* words all over town!

There's **fur** and **fern** and **fork** and **car**.

There's **shirt** and **turn** and **her** and **star**.

There's **start** and **stork** and **barn** and **corn**.

There's **surf** and **herd** and **porch** and **horn**.

Bossy *r,* bossy *r,* give a great cheer

For the **sharpest** sound you ever will hear!

Make a list of other bossy-*r* words. Then use them in your cheer.

Stan the Pest

by Pamela Chanko
illustrated by Amy Wummer

Phonics Fact

St is a blend. Blends are two consonants whose sounds are blended together when you say them. You can hear the *st* blend at the beginning of **Stan** and **still**. What other *st* words can you find in this story? Look at the pictures, too!

Stan was a boy who **just** loved to get attention. He could never sit **still**.

Stacy was **Stan's** big **sister**. She **just** thought **Stan** was a **pest**.

Phonics Fact

The *st* sound can also come at the end of a word, as in **pest**. Can you find a word on this page that ends with *st*?
(Answer: **first**)

Every day, **Stan** tried a new **stunt**.
First, he **stood** on his head.

But **Stacy just** said, "**Stop** it, **Stan**."

Next, **Stan** tried walking on **stilts**.

But **Stacy just** said, "**Stop** it, **Stan**."

Phonics Fact

Sometimes the *st* sound comes in the middle of a word, as in **monster** and **sister**.

Next, **Stan** put **sticky stuff** in his hair and pretended to be a **monster**.

But **Stacy just** said, "**Stop** it, **Stan**."

Next, **Stan** made a **stage** from a **stack** of books and pretended to be the **greatest** rock **star** ever.

But **Stacy just** said, "**Stop** it, **Stan**. You are such a **pest**!"

At **last**, **Stan stopped**.
"A **pest**! **Stacy must** not want me around,"
he thought.
So **Stan** went up the **stairs** to his own room.

That night, there was a big **storm**. When **Stacy** heard the thunder **start**, she was scared to be alone.

"**Stan**! Come here **fast**!" she called.

Stan did all his **funniest stunts** for **Stacy**.
He didn't **stop** until the **storm** was over.
"**Stan**, you may be a **pest**," **Stacy** said.
"But you're also the **best** brother ever!"

ST Riddles

Listen to the riddles. Then match each riddle with the right *st* word from the box. (Hint: Sometimes the *st* appears in the middle or at the end of the word.)

Word Box

stop	stairs	pest	monster	fast
stilts	sister	storm	best	star

1. It is the opposite of *brother*.
2. This kind of weather might have rain or snow.
3. It is the opposite of *go*.
4. You can walk on these to look taller.
5. If you see one in the night sky, you can make a wish on it.
6. It is a scary make-believe creature.
7. You can walk up them or down them.
8. This word means the opposite of *worst*.
9. You move this way when you run quickly.
10. This word describes someone who bothers you.

Answers: 1. sister 2. storm 3. stop 4. stilts 5. star 6. monster 7. stairs 8. best 9. fast 10. pest

ST Cheer

Hooray for *s-t,* the best sound around!

Let's holler *s-t* words all over town!

There's **stop** and **stuff** and **storm** and **pest**.

There's **stilts** and **stunts** and **stairs** and **best**.

There's **sister**, **monster**, **still**, and **fast**.

There's **star** and **sticky**, **first** and **last**.

S-t, s-t, give a great cheer,

For the **most stylish** sound you ever will hear!

Make a list of other *st* words. Then use them in your cheer.

Phonics Tales!™

sk

Skippy Skunk

by Maria Fleming
illustrated by Jackie Snider

Phonics Fact

Sk is a blend. Blends are two consonants whose sounds are blended together when you say them. You can hear the *sk* blend at the beginning of **Skippy**, **skunk**, **skills**, and **sketch**. What other *sk* words can you find in this story? Look at the pictures, too!

Skippy Skunk has many **skills**. **Skippy Skunk** can **sketch** pictures.

Phonics Fact

Sometimes the *sk* blend comes at the end of a word, as in **mask**. Can you find another word on this page that ends in the *sk* blend? Be on the lookout for more!

(Answer: **desk**)

Skippy Skunk can make **masks**. **Skippy Skunk** can do **skits**.

Skippy Skunk can **skate**. **Skippy Skunk** can **ski**.

Skippy Skunk can even **skydive**! But there is one **skill Skippy** does not have.

Skippy Skunk can not **skip**! Every time **Skippy** tries to **skip**, he trips and **skins** his knee.

One day, a **skinny skunk** in a purple **skirt** **skipped** by. Her name was **Skylar**.

"Can I **ask** you a favor?" said **Skippy**.
"Will you teach me to **skip** like you?"
"Sure," said **Skylar**. "That will be an easy **task**."

Then **Skylar** taught **Skippy** a special song to help him **skip**.

Skippy sang **Skylar's skipping** song as he tried to **skip**. **Skippy** did not trip. **Skippy** did not **skin** his knee.

Skippy Skunk was **skipping**! Before long, **Skippy** was **skipping** as **skillfully** as **Skylar**!

Skippy wanted to thank **Skylar** for teaching him to **skip**. But how?

"I know!" said **Skippy**. "**Skylar**, would you like to learn a new **skill**?"
"Sure," said **Skylar**.

So **Skippy Skunk** took **Skylar skydiving**.
Now they both have a brand new **skill**.
And a brand new friend!

SK Riddles

Listen to the riddles. Then match each riddle with the right *sk* word from the box. (Hint: Sometimes the *sk* appears at the end of the word.)

Word Box

skip	skinny	skunk	task	sky
sketch	skin	desk	skirt	skis

1. Girls might wear this instead of pants or shorts.
2. It's a job you have to do.
3. This animal can have a bad smell.
4. It's usually blue and sometimes has clouds.
5. This covers your whole body.
6. It means the same thing as *draw*.
7. It is the opposite of *fat*.
8. This is where you sit at school.
9. It rhymes with *trip*.
10. You wear these to zip down a snowy mountain.

Answers: 1. skirt 2. task 3. skunk 4. sky 5. skin 6. sketch 7. skinny 8. desk 9. skip 10. skis

SK Cheer

Hooray for *s-k,* the best sound around!

Let's holler *s-k* words all over town!

There's **skunk** and **skip** and **skit** and **mask**.

There's **skin** and **sketch** and **desk** and **task**.

There's **skate** and **sky** and **skill** and **dusk**.

There's **skirt** and **skull** and **ski** and **tusk**.

S-k, s-k, shout hip-hip-hooray,

For a sound that takes great **skill** to say!

Make a list of other *sk* words. Then use them in your cheer.

The Princess and the Pretzel

by Violet Findley
illustrated by Richard Torrey

Phonics Fact

Pr is a blend. Blends are two consonants whose sounds are blended together when you say them. You can hear the *pr* blend at the beginning of **prince** and **Preston**. What other *pr* words can you find in this story? Look at the pictures, too!

Once upon a time, in the kingdom of **Princeton**, lived a **prince** named **Preston**.

Each day, **Preston** fed his pet **prairie** dog. He **practiced** karate. He **pruned** the flowers on his **property**.

Life was **pretty** great, except for one **problem**. **Preston** wanted to get married. But he could not find a real **princess** anywhere in **Princeton**.

Then one stormy night, someone **pressed** **Preston's** doorbell. **Prrring, prrring**! When he opened the door, **Preston** saw a **pretty** girl!

"I am **Princess Prudence**, but my friends call me **Prue**," she said. "It's **pretty** stormy. May I stay in your castle tonight?"

"Of course," said **Preston**.

Preston made **Prue** some **prune** tea. Was she a real **princess** or just **pretending**? **Preston** had a **foolproof** plan to find out.

Preston excused himself to **prepare Prue's** room. First, he put a **pretzel** on the bed. Then he covered the **pretzel** with 100 **pretty** quilts.

"Good night, **Prue**," said **Preston**.

But **Prue** did not have a good night. In fact, poor **Prue** woke up as twisted as a **pretzel**!

The next day, **Preston** said, "I don't mean to **pry**, but how did you sleep?"
"**Pretty** badly!" **proclaimed Prue**. "That was **probably** the lumpiest bed in all of **Princeton**!"

Wow! At last, **Preston** had **proof** that **Prue** was not **pretending**. Only a real **princess** could feel a **pretzel** under 100 **pretty** quilts!

Preston told **Prue** about his **pretzel prank** and said he was sorry. Then **Preston** **promptly proposed**.

After that, **Prue promised** to marry **Preston**. And **Preston promised** to never ever put a **pretzel** in **Prue's** bed again.

PR Riddles

Listen to the riddles. Then match each riddle with the right *pr* word from the box.

Word Box

pretty	present	pry	property	prune
prince	pretzel	princess	prairie dog	prize

1. This snack is twisted and salty.
2. It means almost the same thing as *beautiful*.
3. This *pr* word rhymes with *cry*.
4. When something belongs to you, it is called this.
5. When you go to a birthday party, this is what you bring.

6. This furry wild animal lives in a hole.
7. You might get this if you win a contest.
8. The son of a king and queen is called this.
9. The daughter of a king and queen is called this.
10. This dried fruit is bigger than a raisin.

Answers: 1. pretzel 2. pretty 3. pry 4. property 5. present 6. prairie dog 7. prize 8. prince 9. princess 10. prune

PR Cheer

Hooray for *p-r,* the best sound around!

Let's holler *p-r* words all over town!

There's **prune** and **praise** and **pride** and **propel**.

There's **pretzel** and **problem** and **price** as well.

There's **prompt** and **prize** and **proof** and **Prue**.

There's **press** and **prince** and **princess**, too.

P-r, p-r, give a great cheer,

For the **prettiest** sound you'll ever hear!

Make a list of other *pr* words. Then use them in your cheer.

Clark and Cleo's Clouds

by Elizabeth Bennett
illustrated by Kelly Kennedy

Phonics Fact

Cl is a blend. Blends are two consonants whose sounds are blended together when you say them. You can hear the *cl* blend at the beginning of **Clark** and **Cleo**. What other *cl* words can you find in this story? Look at the pictures, too!

One day, **Clark** and his sister, **Cleo**, went to **Clovis** Park.

They **climbed** a hill and had a picnic **close** to a pretty lake.

Clark and **Cleo** thought the **clam** chowder was especially delicious!

After a while, a **cluster** of **clouds cluttered** the **clear** sky.

"Guess what I see?" said **Clark**, staring up at the **clouds**. "Here is a **clue**: He has a round nose and **clomps** around in huge shoes."

Phonics Fact

Sometimes the *cl* can come in the middle of a word, as in **exclaimed**.

"You see a **clown**!" said **Cleo.**
"Very **clever**!" **exclaimed Clark**.

Another **cluster** of **clouds** appeared.
"Guess what I see?" said **Cleo**. "Here is a **clue**:
You hang them up in a **closet**."

"You see **clothes**!" said **Clark**.
"Very **clever**!" **exclaimed Cleo**.

Another **cluster** of **clouds** appeared. "Guess what I see?" said **Clark**. "Here is a **clue**: If you find one in a **clump** of grass, you will have good luck."

"You see a four-leaf **clover**!" said **Cleo**.
"Very **clever**!" **exclaimed Clark**.

Another **cluster** of **clouds** appeared.
"Guess what I see?" said **Cleo**. "Here is a **clue**:
She **claps** when we **clean** our rooms."

"You see Mom!" said **Clark** with a giggle.
"Very **clever**!" **exclaimed Cleo**.

"Hey, Mom is pointing to a **cloud clock**.
I think she wants us to **close** up our picnic basket and come home," **Cleo** told **Clark**.
So they did!

CL Riddles

Listen to the riddles. Then match each riddle with the right *cl* word from the box.

Word Box

clam	clown	clap	clover	close
clean	clue	climb	clock	clothes

1. You do this with your hands at the end of a play.
2. This sea creature lives in a shell.
3. It is the opposite of *dirty*.
4. It is the opposite of *open*.
5. You wear them every day.
6. You look at this to find out the time.
7. At the circus, he makes you laugh.
8. You do this to get to the top of the stairs.
9. You use this to solve a mystery.
10. If you find one with four-leaves, it will bring you luck.

Answers: 1. clap 2. clam 3. clean 4. close 5. clothes 6. clock 7. clown 8. climb 9. clue 10. clover

CL Cheer

Hooray for *c-l*, the best sound around!

Let's holler *c-l* words all over town!

There's **cliff** and **clash** to name a few,

Clown and **clog** and **cloud** and **clue**.

There's **clock** and **club** to shout out loud,

Clean and **clang** and **clothes** and **cloud**!

C-l, c-l, **clap** and cheer,

For the **classiest** sound you ever will hear!

Make a list of other *cl* words. Then use them in your cheer.

gr

A Groundhog Named Grady

by Teddy Slater
illustrated by Tammie Lyon

Phonics Fact

Gr is a blend. Blends are two consonants whose sounds are blended together when you say them. You can hear the *gr* blend at the beginning of **Grady**, **groundhog**, and **great**. What other *gr* words can you find in this story? Look at the pictures, too!

Grady was a little **groundhog.** He lived with his family in a **great** big hole in the **ground**.

Grady had a mom, a dad, a **grandma**, and a **grandpa**. He also had a big brother and sister named **Grover** and **Grace**.

They all thought **Grady** was the **greatest** little **groundhog** in the world. Except for one thing. . . .

Grady was a **grabber**! **Grady grabbed** all the **grapes** out of **Grandma's** fruit bowl.

Grady grabbed Grace's green balloon.

And **Grady** was always **grabbing Grover's** toy **grizzly** bear.

Once **Grady** even **grabbed Grandpa's** whiskers.
"Ouch!" **Grandpa groaned**.

"**Grady**," **Grandpa grumbled**. "Would you please stop **grabbing** everything!"
But **Grady** just **grinned**. Then he **grabbed** **Grandma's** glasses.

One day, **Grady's** whole family went for a **group** walk in **Greenwood Grove**.

A **great** big rosebush was **growing** by a **gravel** path. **Grady** reached out to **grab** a flower. "Be careful!" **Grandma** warned.

But it was too late. **Grady grabbed** the thorny stem.
"OUCH!" **Grady groaned**.

"Poor **Grady**!" cried **Grace**, **Grover**, Mom,
Dad, **Grandma**, and **Grandpa** all together.
No one said, "That's what you get for **grabbing**."
They didn't have to.

From then on, **Grady** never **grabbed** anything again. Well, hardly ever!

GR Riddles

Listen to the riddles. Then match each riddle with the right *gr* word from the box.

Word Box				
grow	grasshopper	grapes	Grace	green
gray	groundhog	grandma	grin	grass

1. There will be six more weeks of winter if this animal sees its shadow.
2. Peas are this color.
3. This fruit comes in bunches.
4. This is another word for *smile*.
5. This girl's name rhymes with *place*.
6. This grows all over the ground.

7. Little Red Riding Hood went to visit her.
8. When you water a plant, it does this.
9. You get this color when you mix black and white paint.
10. This green insect likes to jump.

Answers: 1. groundhog 2. green 3. grapes 4. grin 5. Grace 6. grass 7. grandma 8. grow 9. gray 10. grasshopper

GR Cheer

Hooray for *g-r,* the best sound around!

Let's holler *g-r* words all over town!

There's **green** and **grab** and **grass** and **grandma**.

There's **grow** and **group** and **grapes** and **grandpa**.

There's **grouch** and **gray** and more words still—

Like **grouch** and **greet** and **gross** and **grill**.

G-r, g-r, give a **great** cheer,

For the **grandest** sound you ever will hear!

Make a list of other *gr* words. Then use them in your cheer.

Flora Flamingo Learns to Fly

by Maria Fleming
illustrated by Kellie Lewis

Phonics Fact

Fl is a blend. Blends are two consonants whose sounds are blended together when you say them. You can hear the *fl* blend at the beginning of **fluffy**, **Flora**, **flamingo**, and **fly**. What other *fl* words can you find in this story? Look at the pictures, too!

Fluffy little **Flora Flamingo** cannot **fly**.

Every day, **Flora** tries to **fly** but fails.
Flap, flap, flap. . . **flop**. **Flap, flap, flap**. . . **flop**.

Flora is upset. She wants to **fly** to the **flamingo** festival in **Florida** with the rest of the **flamingo flock**.

Phonics Fact

Sometimes the *fl* blend comes in the middle of a word, as in **butterflies**. Can you spot another word in this story that has the *fl* blend in the middle? (Answer: **fireflies**)

Flora watches the **butterflies**.
They **flutter** from **flower** to **flower**.

Flora tries to **fly** like the **butterflies**.
But it's no use.
Flap, **flap**, **flap**...**flop**. **Flap**, **flap**, **flap**...**flop**.

At night, **Flora** watches the **fireflies**. They **flicker** and **flash** as they **flit** through the air.

Flora tries to **fly** like the **fireflies**.
But it's no use.
Flap, **flap**, **flap**. . . **flop**. **Flap**, **flap**, **flap**. . . **flop**.

Flora's friend **Floyd Flounder floats** by.
"I'm a **flop** at **flying**," **Flora** tells **Floyd**.

"Just be patient," says **Floyd**. "Soon you will **fly** like the rest of the **flamingo flock**." **Flora** hopes **Floyd** is right.

One morning, **Flora** wakes up. Her **fluff** is gone!
Now she has **flashy** pink feathers!

Will the feathers help **Flora fly**?
Flap, **flap**, **flap**...

Flap, **flap**, **flap**, **flap**, **flap**, **flap**!
They do! **Flora** is not a **flop** at **flying** after all!

Soon it is time for all the **flamingos** to **fly** to **Florida**. Who will lead the **flock**? **Flora**, of course! And her **flying** is **FLAWLESS**!

FL Riddles

Listen to the riddles. Then match each riddle with the right *fl* word from the box.

Word Box				
float	flamingo	flop	flapjack	flounder
flowers	Florida	flash	flap	flock

1. You put these in a vase.
2. This kind of bird is big and pink.
3. A firefly's light does this at night.
4. This is a state in our country.
5. Boats do this on water.
6. It rhymes with *stop*.
7. This is what a group of birds is called.
8. It is another word for *pancake*.
9. This is a kind of fish.
10. Birds do this with their wings to fly.

Answers: 1. flowers 2. flamingo 3. flash 4. Florida 5. float 6. flop 7. flock 8. flapjack 9. flounder 10. flap

FL Cheer

Hooray for *f-l*, the best sound around!

Let's holler *f-l* words all over town!

There's **flap** and **flop** and **flower** and **flu**.

There's **fluff** and **flamingo** and **flutter**, too!

There's **fly** and **flock** and **float** and **floor**.

There's **flute** and **flag** and many more!

F-l, f-l, give a great cheer,

For the most **flawless** sound you ever will hear!

Make a list of other *fl* words. Then use them in your cheer.

The Trolls Take a Trip

by Maria Fleming
illustrated by Doug Jones

Phonics Fact

Tr is a blend. Blends are two consonants whose sounds are blended together when you say them. You can hear the *tr* blend at the beginning of **trolls**, **tradition**, **trip**, and **trout**. What other *tr* words can you find in this story? Look at the pictures, too!

The **trolls** have a **tradition**. Every summer, they make a **trip** to Lake **Trout**.

The **trolls travel** to Lake **Trout** from near and far.

They **travel** by **truck** and **trailer**.

They **travel** by **train** and by **trolley**. Some **trolls** even **travel** by **tractor**!

The **trolls** bring **trays** of **treats**. They have a picnic under the **trees**.

The **trolls** fish in Lake **Trout**.

The **trolls** play games and **try** to win **trophies**.

Their favorite game is racing **tricycles** around a **track**.

At night, the **trolls** play **trumpets** and **trombones**.

The **trolls** sing and dance.
They have **tremendous** fun.

At the end of the **trip**, the **trolls** get back into their **trucks** and **trailers**.

They get back onto the **trains**, **trolleys**, and **tractors**.

Then the **trolls travel** home with memories to **treasure**. They would not **trade** their **tradition** for anything—not even a **trillion** dollars!

TR Riddles

Listen to the riddles. Then match each riddle with the right *tr* word from the box.

Word Box

trip	treat	train	tree	trumpet
tractor	trout	trolley	trophy	tray

1. This is something tall that grows.
2. You find this vehicle on a farm.
3. It rhymes with *jolly*.
4. This is a kind of fish.
5. You play music on this.
6. It is something tasty to eat.
7. This moves along tracks.
8. This is flat and you carry things on it.
9. It rhymes with *rip*.
10. This is a kind of prize.

Answers: 1. tree 2. tractor 3. trolley 4. trout 5. trumpet 6. treat 7. train 8. tray 9. trip 10. trophy

TR Cheer

Hooray for *t-r,* the best sound around!

Let's holler *t-r* words all over town!

There's **troll** and **trip** and **tree** and **true**.

There's **truck** and **train** and **treasure**, too!

There's **track** and **treat** and **trash** and **tray**.

There's **trot** and **trick** and **trap**—hooray!

T-r, t-r, give a great cheer,

For the most **tremendous** sound you ever will hear!

Make a list of other *tr* words. Then use them in your cheer.

Phonics Tales!™

sl

Sleepyhead Sloth

by Violet Findley

illustrated by Doug Jones

Phonics Fact

Sl is a blend. Blends are two consonants whose sounds are blended together when you say them. You can hear the *sl* blend at the beginning of **Sloth** and **Slinky**. What other *sl* words can you find in this story? Look at the pictures, too!

Meet **Sloth**. Meet his pal, **Slinky**.

Slinky tries everything to wake **Sloth** from his **slumber**.

Slinky slithers over in **slick** sunglasses and starts playing the bongo drums. **Slap**! **Slap**! **Slap**!

But **sleepyhead Sloth** keeps snoozing!

Slinky slithers over and offers **Sloth** a **slurp** of his milkshake and a big **sloppy slice** of pizza.

But **sleepyhead Sloth** keeps snoozing!

Slinky slides over and invites **Sloth** to go **sledding** on **Slippery Slope** with their **slug** friend named **Slimy**.

But **sleepyhead Sloth** keeps snoozing!

Slinky slithers over and shouts, "Wake up **Sloth**, I'm having a party in my tree!"

But **sleepyhead Sloth** keeps snoozing!

Then **Slinky** adds **slyly**, "Did I mention that it's a **SLEEPOVER** party?"

Sloth opens his eyes a **sliver** and
slowly smiles.

Then **Sloth** says, "Let me get my **slippers**.
I do so love **sleepovers**!"

SL Riddles

Listen to the riddles. Then match each riddle with the right *sl* word from the box.

Word Box				
sloth	sleep	slick	sled	slippers
slurp	sloppy	slice	slow	slide

1. You use this to slide down snowy hills.
2. It is the opposite of *fast*.

3. You slip down this at the playground.
4. You put these on your feet at night.

5. A piece of pizza is sometimes called this.
6. Babies do this in their cribs.
7. It is the opposite of *neat*.
8. This word rhymes with *click*.

9. This slow-moving animal lives in the rainforest.
10. It is not polite to drink this way.

Answers: 1. sled 2. slow 3. slide 4. slippers 5. slice 6. sleep 7. sloppy 8. slick 9. sloth 10. slurp

SL Cheer

Hooray for *s-l*, the best sound around!

Let's holler *s-l* words all over town!

There's **sloth** and **sled** and **slush** and **sleek**.

There's **slug** and **slide** and **slap** and **sleep**.

There's **slip** and **slope** and **slug** and **sly**.

There's **slice** and **slow** and **slink**, oh my!

S-l, s-l, give a great cheer,

For the **slickest** sound you ever will hear!

Make a list of other *sl* words. Then use them in your cheer.

Phonics Tales!™

ch

Chimp and Chick's Lunch

by Liza Charlesworth
illustrated by Jannie Ho

Phonics Fact

Ch is a digraph. Digraphs are two letters put together to make a single sound, such as the *ch* sound in **chilly**, **chick**, and **chimp**. What other *ch* words can you find in this story? Look at the pictures, too!

One **chilly** day, **Chick** went to visit his **chum**, **Chimp**.

Chimp and **Chick chatted**. They played **chess** and **checkers**. They read a **chapter** book. All of this made the two **chums** very hungry!

Phonics Fact

The digraph *ch* can also appear at the end of a word such as **lunch**. Can you find another word on this page that ends in *ch*? Check the rest of the story, too! (Answer: **munch**)

So **Chimp** and **Chick** decided to make some **lunch**.
"What should we **munch**?" **cheeped Chick**.
"You **choose**," answered **Chimp**.

"OK," **cheeped Chick**. "I **choose**
cheddar cheese!"
So **Chimp** got **cheddar cheese**.

"I **choose cherries**!" **cheeped Chick**.
So **Chimp** got **cherries**.

"I **choose chili**!" **cheeped Chick**.
So **Chimp** got **chili**.

"I **choose chips**!" **cheeped Chick**.
So **Chimp** got **chips**.

"I **choose chestnuts**!" **cheeped Chick**.
So **Chimp** got **chestnuts**.

"I **choose chocolate**!" **cheeped Chick**.
So **Chimp** got **chocolate**.

“This food looks delicious,” said **Chimp cheerfully**.
“But how do we turn it into our **lunch**?”
“I have an idea!” **cheeped Chick**.

Chick took the **cheddar cheese** and **cherries** and **chili** and **chips** and **chestnuts** and **chocolate** and made a huge **sandwich**!

Chimp poured some **punch**. Then the two **chums** plopped down in **chairs** and shared the **sandwich**. **Crunch, crunch, crunch, crunch**!

"Mmmm! What a **charming** meal!"
cheeped Chick.
"Yes," **chuckled Chimp**. "It's the best **lunch**
I have ever **munched**!"

CH Riddles

Listen to the riddles. Then match each with the right *ch* word from the box. (Hint: Sometimes the *ch* appears at the end of the word.)

Word Box

chick	cheese	cherry	checkers	chair
chuckle	chimp	chilly	lunch	crunch

1. This is another name for *monkey*.
2. It means almost the same thing as *laugh*.
3. This sweet, red fruit is small with a long stem.
4. One person can sit on it.
5. You eat this meal in the middle of the day.
6. People put this on top of pizza and burgers.
7. This sound is made when you bite into an apple.
8. This board game has red and black playing pieces.
9. It means almost the same thing as *cold*.
10. This is the name for a baby chicken.

Answers: 1. chimp 2. chuckle 3. cherry 4. chair 5. lunch 6. cheese 7. crunch 8. checkers 9. chilly 10. chick

CH Cheer

Hooray for *c-h,* the best sound around!

Let's holler *c-h* words all over town!

There's **chimp** and **chick** and **chair** and **chore**.

There's **charm** and **child** and so many more—

Like **chip** and **cheese** and **brunch** and **lunch**

And **rich** and **peach** and **munch** and **crunch**!

C-h, c-h, give a great **cheer**,

For the most **charming** sound you ever will hear!

Make a list of other words that have *ch* at the beginning or the end. Then use them in your cheer.

Shelly's New Shoes

by Pamela Chanko
illustrated by Doug Jones

Phonics Fact

Sh is a digraph. Digraphs are two letters put together to make a single sound, such as the *sh* sound in **Shelly**, **shirt**, and **shorts**. What other *sh* words can you find in this story? Look at the pictures, too!

This is **Shelly**. **She** has a favorite **shirt** and **shorts**.

Shelly also has some favorite **shoes**. **She** thinks they are really **sharp**!

Phonics Fact

The *sh* sound can also come in the middle of a word, as in **pushed**.

One day, **Shelly** got a **shock**. She **pushed** and **shoved** her feet into her **shoes**. But her **shoes** did not fit!

Phonics Fact

Sometimes the *sh* sound comes at the end of a word, as in **trash**.

"These **shoes** are going in the **trash**!" Mom said.
"No!" **shouted Shelly**.

"We **should** go **shopping**," Mom said. So **she** grabbed **Shelly** and **dashed** to **Sherman's** **shoe shop**.

"I have many **shoes** to **show** you," said the **shopkeeper**. "We have **shelves** and **shelves** of **shoes**!"

First, he **showed Shelly** some fancy **shoes**.
"Too **shiny**!" **she** said.

Then, he **showed Shelly** some pointy **shoes**.
"I don't like the **shape**!" **she** said.

Next, he **showed Shelly** some sandals covered in **seashells**.
"These **crush** my toes!" **she** said.

Shelly tried on every **shoe** in the **shop**. But the **shoes** were either too **showy**, or too **shaky**, or they gave her a **rash**.

Shelly shut her eyes and **shed** a tear.
"I **wish** I didn't need new **shoes**!" **she** cried.

But then **Shelly** spotted one last pair on the top **shelf** in the **shadows**.
"**Gosh**," said Mom, "those look just like your old **shoes**!"

"I know. They are really **sharp**!" **gushed Shelly**. "We'll take the red **shoes**," said Mom to the **shopkeeper**. "Isn't that a **shock**?"

SH Riddles

Listen to the riddles. Then match each with the right *sh* word from the box. (Hint: Sometimes the *sh* appears at the end of the word.)

Word Box

cash	shut	fish	shelf	shorts
wish	shoes	shirt	ship	shape

1. You wear these on your feet.
2. This animal has gills and swims.
3. You make one when you blow out your birthday candles.
4. It has sleeves and a collar.
5. You wear these when it's too hot for long pants.
6. This is another word for *money*.
7. You can put books on this.
8. This word means the opposite of *open*.
9. It sails across the sea.
10. It can be a triangle, a square, or a circle.

Answers: 1. shoes 2. fish 3. wish 4. shirt 5. shorts 6. cash 7. shelf 8. shut 9. ship 10. shape

SH Cheer

Hooray for *s-h,* the best sound around!

Let's holler *s-h* words all over town!

There's **shoe** and **shelf** and **splash** and **wish**.

There's **shop** and **shirt** and **push** and **fish**.

There's **shell** and **shorts** and **crush** and **dash**.

There's **shape** and **ship** and **shout** and **smash**.

S-h, s-h, give a great cheer,

For the **shiniest** sound you ever will hear!

Make a list of other words that have *sh* at the beginning or the end. Then use them in your cheer.

The Thing That Went Thump

by Maria Fleming
illustrated by Stephen Lewis

Phonics Fact

Th is a digraph. Digraphs are two letters put together to make a single sound, such as the *th* sound in **Thursday**, **Theo**, and **Thorn**. What other *th* words can you find in this story? Look at the pictures, too!

One **Thursday** night, **Theo Thorn** was very sleepy.

Phonics Fact

The digraph *th* can also appear at the end of a word, as in **bath** and **teeth**.

So **Theo** took a **bath**, brushed his **teeth**, and went to bed early.

Suddenly, **Theo** heard a strange sound.
Thump! **Thump**! **Thud**! **Thump**! **Thump**! **Thud**!

What could it be? **Theo thought** of a **thousand** scary **things**.

Maybe it was a giant **sloth with thick** fur.
Thump! **Thump**! **Thud**!

Maybe it was a wooly **mammoth with** big **teeth**.
Thump! **Thump**! **Thud**!

Maybe it was a monster **with three** heads and **thirty** eyes. **Thump**! **Thump**! **Thud**!

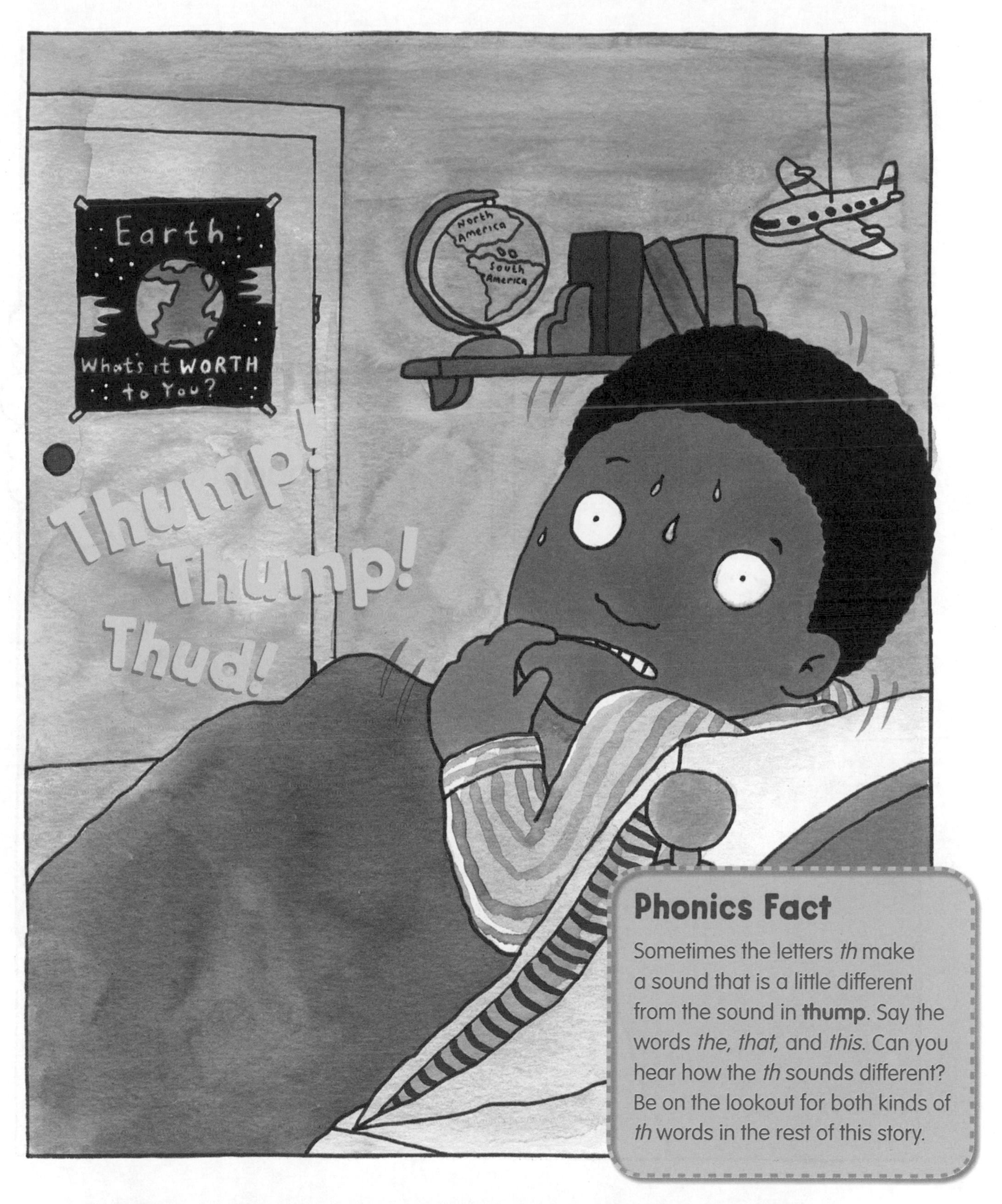

Phonics Fact

Sometimes the letters *th* make a sound that is a little different from the sound in **thump**. Say the words *the, that,* and *this*. Can you hear how the *th* sounds different? Be on the lookout for both kinds of *th* words in the rest of this story.

THUMP! **THUMP**! **THUD**! **THUMP**! **THUMP**! **THUD**!
The **thumping thing** was getting closer!

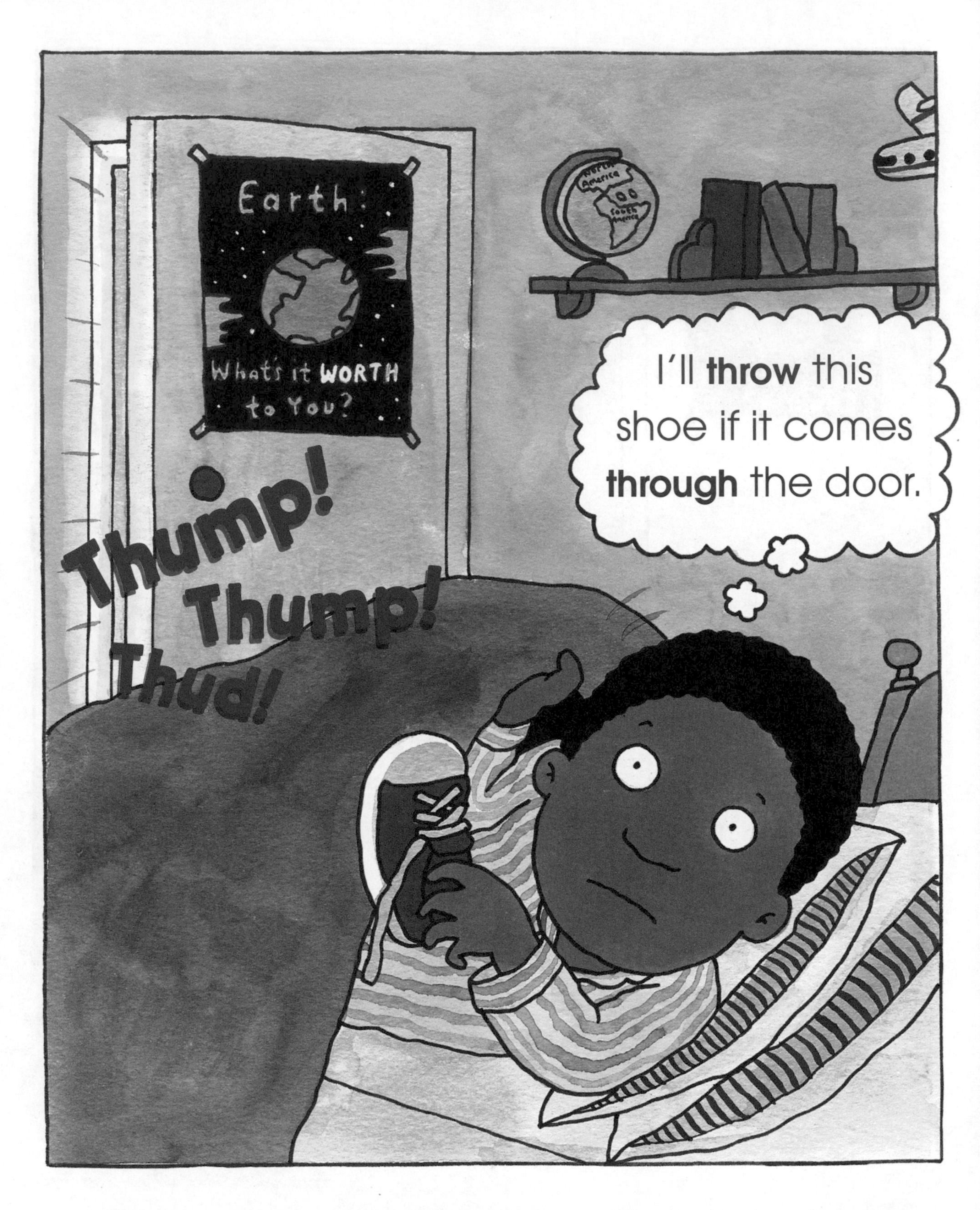

Theo hid **beneath** the covers. He held his **breath**. Suddenly, the door burst open. In **thumped**...

…**Theo's** sister!
"**Ruth**, you scared me to **death**!" said **Theo**.

"Sorry, **Theo**," said **Ruth**. "Will you help me **with** my **math** homework?"

"Okay," said **Theo**.
Theo was **thankful** the **thumping thing** was only his sister.

But he made **Ruth** take an **oath** that she would never scare him like that again.

TH Riddles

Listen to the riddles. Then match each with the right *th* word from the box. (Hint: Sometimes the *th* appears at the end of the word.)

Word Box

Earth	thump	sloth	thorn	bath
Thursday	three	teeth	math	thick

1. This day comes after Wednesday.
2. This is something very pointy.
3. You need these to chew food.
4. This is the opposite of *thin*.
5. This is the planet we live on.
6. This animal moves very slowly.
7. You take this to get clean.
8. You use numbers to do this subject.
9. This loud sound rhymes with *bump*.
10. This number comes after *two*.

Answers: 1. Thursday 2. thorn 3. teeth 4. thick 5. Earth 6. sloth 7. bath 8. math 9. thump 10. three

TH Cheer

Hooray for *t-h,* the best sound around!
Let's holler *t-h* words all over town!

There's **thump** and **thing** and **teeth** and **mouth**.

There's **thumb** and **thorn** and **north** and **south**.

There's **thread** and **throat** and **bath** and **moth**.

There's **think** and **thank** and **math** and **cloth**.

T-h, t-h, give a great cheer,

For the most **thrilling** sound you ever will hear!

Make a list of other words that have *th* at the beginning or the end. Then use them in your cheer.